COMBAT
STUNT PLANES

Published by Top That! Publishing plc
Tide Mill Way, Woodbridge, Suffolk, IP12 1AP, UK
www.topthatpublishing.com
Copyright © 2013 Top That! Publishing plc
All rights reserved.
0 2 4 6 8 9 7 5 3 1
Printed and bound in China

FOLDING TIPS

BEFORE YOU BEGIN ANY OF THE PROJECTS IN THIS SECTION, HERE ARE SOME HELPFUL TIPS THAT WILL MAKE YOUR FOLDING EASIER:

- Before you start folding, make sure your paper is the correct shape.
- Fold on a flat surface, like a table or a book.
- Make your folds and cuts neat and accurate.
- Crease your folds into place by running your thumbnail along them.
- Carefully score along the marked lines using safety scissors and a ruler. This will make folding easier, especially as the lines become obscured toward the end of the model-making.

SYMBOLS AND BASIC FOLDING PROCEDURES

These symbols show the direction in which paper should be folded. Although you'll not use them all in this book, you can use them to make up your own planes.

1. VALLEY FOLD (FOLD IN FRONT)

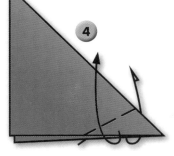

2. MOUNTAIN FOLD (FOLD BEHIND)

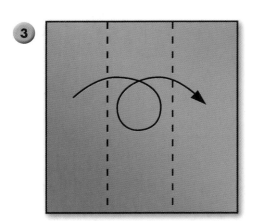

3. FOLD OVER AND OVER

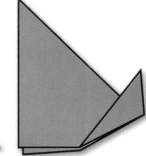

4. OUTSIDE REVERSE FOLD

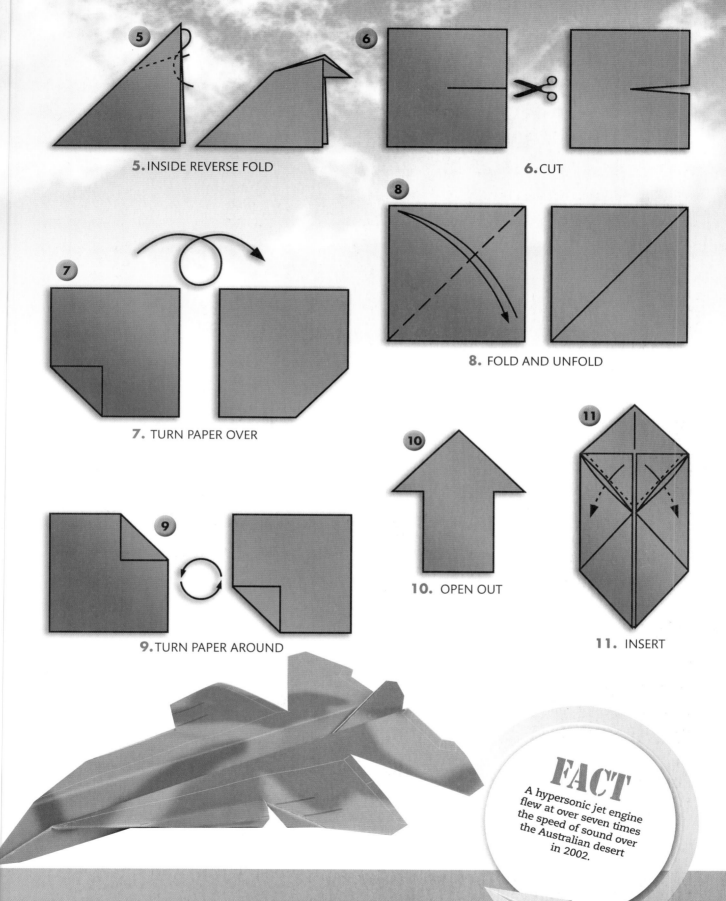

5. INSIDE REVERSE FOLD

6. CUT

7. TURN PAPER OVER

8. FOLD AND UNFOLD

9. TURN PAPER AROUND

10. OPEN OUT

11. INSERT

FACT

A hypersonic jet engine flew at over seven times the speed of sound over the Australian desert in 2002.

HAWKER HUNTER

This fearless combat Fighter is a must on any war mission.

Use the printed page numbered 1 at the back of this book.

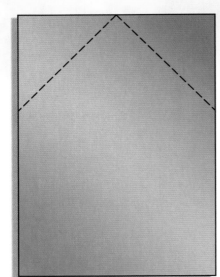

1. Hold the page pattern-side down. Fold in the two top corners along the dotted lines using valley folds.

4. Make mountain folds along the three dashed lines running down the center of the plane. Make sure you form a short valley fold between the two diagonal mountain folds at the rear of the plane.

Cut away the two rear triangles to shape the tail fins. Cut the two small solid lines.

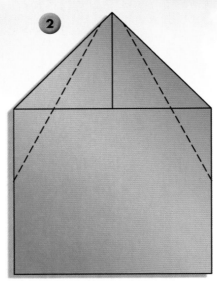

2. Fold along the two diagonal dotted lines, again using valley folds.

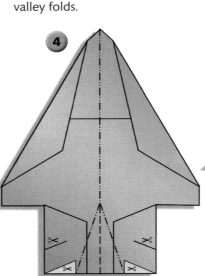

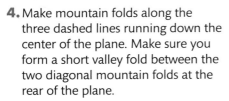

3. Cut along the two solid angled lines, as shown. Now fold in the two flaps, using valley folds, along the dotted lines. Keep these flaps firmly in place throughout the remaining stages.

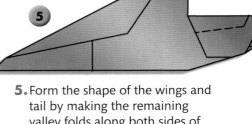

5. Form the shape of the wings and tail by making the remaining valley folds along both sides of the plane.

Hold the base of your plane between your thumb and forefinger and throw quite firmly.

FACT

The Hawker Hunter was the RAF's first single-winged (monoplane) fighter. It had to be fast and accurate to evade enemy fighter attacks and could perform loops and barrel rolls!

To perform a supersonic flight: To make your plane go faster, it needs to have a heavy nose (add a paper clip or sticky putty for weight). Hold the plane above your shoulder and throw hard, with the front slightly raised. To make it fly even faster, try catapulting it with an elastic band!

BAE HAWK 200

Another amazing aircraft made in a few easy steps.

Use the printed page numbered 2 at the back of this book.

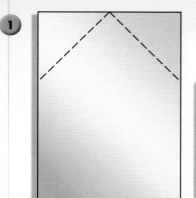

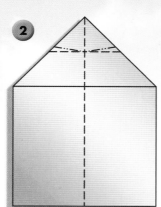

1. Hold the page pattern-side down. Fold in the two top corners along the dotted lines using valley folds.

2. Fold down the top triangle along the dotted line using a valley fold. Next, make two mountain folds along the diagonal dashed lines by folding the pointed tip back on itself. Firmly fold the plane down its center, using a valley fold, ensuring that the folds in the pointed tip stay securely tucked in place.

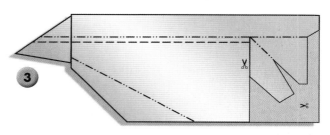

3. Form the tail shape by cutting along the solid lines, as shown. To create the plane's body and wings, bend mountain folds and valley folds along the dotted lines, as shown.

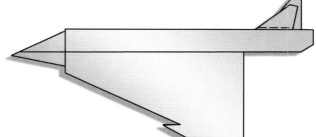

4. Make a cut along the bottom of the wings on the solid line, as shown. Valley fold along the diagonal lines on both sides, to form the wings. Tuck the tail up through the slit at the rear of the plane using a series of inward-facing folds, as shown (right). Bend down the tail fins.

Hold the base of the plane between your thumb and forefinger about 2 inches from the front and gently throw it straight forward.

FACT
The BAE Hawk is used by the British Red Arrows aerobatic display team, which perform an array of stunts in formation.

To perform a formation: Make one or more BAE Hawks and ask a friend to help to launch them at exactly the same time. Experiment and make the cut in step 4 larger, first on one and then the other. Do your planes fly at the same speed and direction? Can you make them perform stunts together?

LOCKHEED MARTIN F-35 LIGHTNING

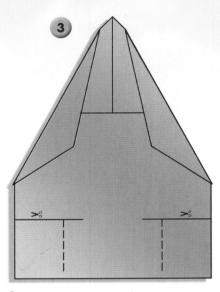

Prepare for combat with this great fighter plane.

Use the printed page numbered 3 at the back of this book.

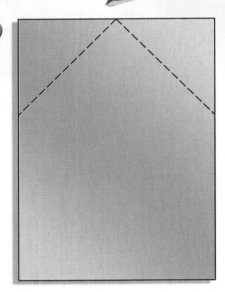

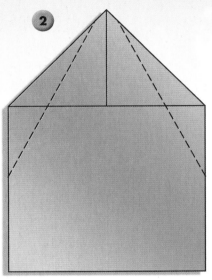

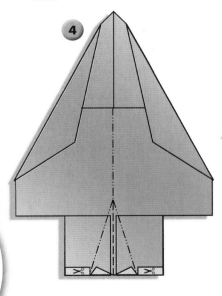

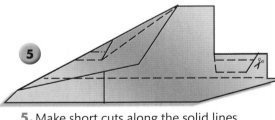

1. Hold the page pattern-side down. Fold in the two top corners along the dotted lines using valley folds.

2. Fold along the two diagonal dotted lines, again using valley folds.

3. Cut along the two short horizontal lines on either side of the plane. Then fold in these tabs along the vertical lines.

4. Cut along the bottom solid lines to cut a rectangle from the rear of the plane. Make mountain folds along the three dashed lines running down the center of the plane. Make sure you form a short valley fold between the two diagonal mountain folds at the rear of the plane.

5. Make short cuts along the solid lines on the wing and tail areas. Using valley folds, form the shape of the plane by folding along the lines, as shown.

To fly your plane, hold it between your forefinger and thumb about 4 inches from the front, and throw it gently.

FACT
The Lockheed Martin F-35 Lightning II is a stealth multi-role aircraft, under development to perform ground attack and defense missions. It is part of the Joint Strike Fighter Program, in which the United States and its allies develop and build aircraft.

6

To perform a nose dive: First, you need to tweak the back of both wings very slightly upward. This stunt relies on how you throw the plane. Hold the aircraft about 4 inches from the front and throw it gently, either on a flat, or slightly upward angle. The plane should pitch upward, but not so much so that it completes a loop. Instead, it should fall back to the ground, completing a nose dive.

LOCKHEED NIGHTHAWK

This streamlined fighter will glide into action with the greatest of ease.

Use the printed page numbered 4 at the back of this book.

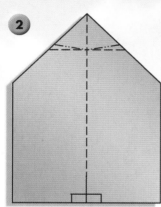

1. Hold the page pattern-side down. Fold in the two top corners along the dotted lines using valley folds. Make three vertical cuts at the bottom along the solid lines. Bend the outside flaps under using mountain folds. Then bend the inside flaps up by using valley folds.

2. Fold down the top triangle using a valley fold. Next, make two mountain folds along the diagonal lines by folding the pointed tip back on itself. Firmly fold the plane down its center, using a valley fold, ensuring that the folds in the pointed tip stay securely tucked in place.

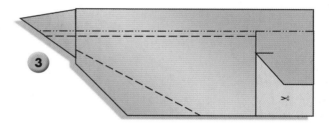

3. Using the solid lines as your guide, cut away the area around the tail of the plane. Make a series of mountain folds and valley folds to form the shape of the plane, as shown. Tuck the tail up through the slit at the rear of the plane using a mountain fold on each side, as shown.

4. Fold up the wing tips using valley folds along the dotted lines. Secure the tail by tucking the flap from one side around the other and interlock them.

   To fly your plane hold it 2 inches from the front and throw it gently forward.

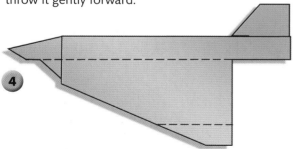

FACT

Although it is known as a stealth fighter, the Lockheed Nighthawk is actually more of a bomber. The flat surfaces deflect radar and its engines are shielded to reduce heat emissions so it can attack undetected.

To perform a glide: This bomber plane needs to fly undetected. Silently glide through the air by making your plane as lightweight as possible. Hold it 2 inches from the front and hold the plane in front of your shoulder. Throw it gently forward.

B-2 SPIRIT

This unusual-looking plane makes a great fighter.

Use the printed page numbered 5 at the back of this book.

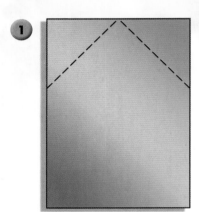

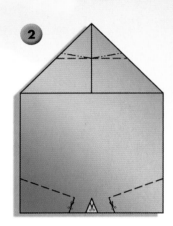

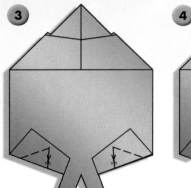

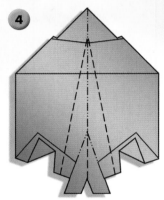

1. Hold the page pattern-side down. Fold in the two top corners using valley folds.

2. Fold down the top triangle using a valley fold. Next, make two mountain folds along the dashed lines by folding the pointed tip back on itself. Cut out the tail using the solid lines as your guide. Valley fold along the diagonal dotted lines to form the rear of the wings.

3. Cut two slits along the solid lines. Then, using valley folds, bend along the diagonal lines, as shown.

4. Firmly fold the plane down its center using a mountain fold, ensuring that the folds in the pointed tip stay securely tucked in place. Make sure you form a short valley fold between the two diagonal mountain folds at the rear. Fold down the wings along the long diagonals.

5. To form the main body and wings, use a series of valley and mountain folds, as shown. Open out the tail fins.

   To fly your plane, hold it about 2 inches from the front and throw it gently forward.

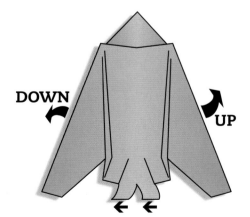

DOWN   **UP**

8

To perform a boomerang: The boomerang throw enables your aircraft to fly forward and then turn back (perfect for carrying out secret radar missions). If you are looking at the plane from the back, tweak the back of both tail fins slightly to the left. Then, fold the right wing upward across its entire length. Finally, fold the left wing downward across its entire length. Throw the plane at shoulder height slightly to the right.

BAE SEA HARRIER

This jump jet gets straight off the ground.

Use the printed page numbered 6 at the back of this book.

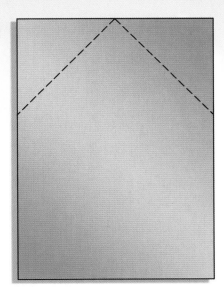

1. Hold the page pattern-side down. Fold in the two top corners along the dotted lines using valley folds.

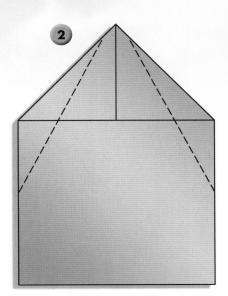

2. Fold along the two diagonal dotted lines, again using valley folds.

4. Cut out two small rectangles at the bottom by following the solid lines. Make mountain folds along the dashed lines and valley folds along the dotted lines to form the shape of the plane, as shown.

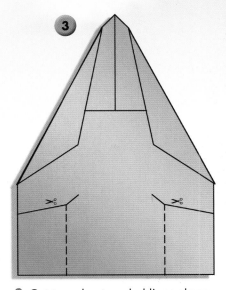

3. Cut two short angled lines along the solid lines on either side. Fold these flaps over using valley folds along the vertical lines, as shown. Make sure these flaps are kept tucked in for all of the following steps.

To fly your plane, hold it about 2 inches from the front and throw it gently forward.

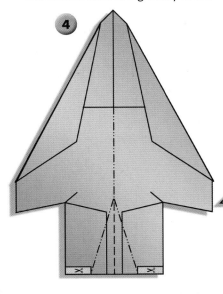

5. Make small slits by cutting along the solid lines on the wings and tail section, as shown. Using valley folds, create the main shape of the body and wings.

FACT

The Sea Harrier is a naval jet fighter and first entered the Royal Navy in 1980 and retired in 2006. It provided air defense for the carrier fleet against low-flying air combat. It was designed for air-to-air combat, but also surveillance missions, air-to-ground and air-to-sea attacks.

To perform a vertical take-off: The Sea Harriers need short take-offs! Try placing your Sea Harrier above an electric fan on a slow speed for some much-needed vertical lift! This will help the aircraft to gain height and remain in the air. (This is also great for glides!)

PANAVIA TORNADO IDS

This speedy fighter can be created in minutes.

Use the printed page numbered 7 at the back of this book.

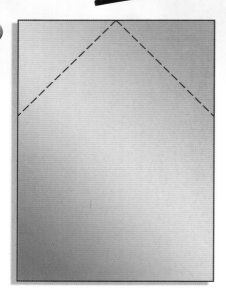

1. Hold the page pattern-side down. Fold in the two top corners along the dotted lines using valley folds.

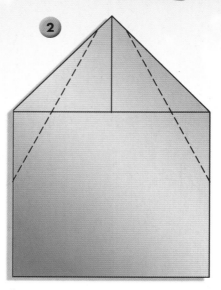

2. Fold along the two diagonal dotted lines, again using valley folds.

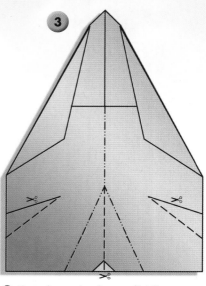

3. Cut along the four solid lines, as shown. Make mountain folds and valley folds to form the shape of the plane.

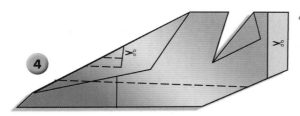

4. Cut off the end of the tail along the solid line. Then, cut small slits on the wings along the solid lines, as shown. Using valley folds, form the tail, wing, and body section.

To fly your plane, hold it about 4 inches from the front and throw gently forward.

FACT

The Tornado is a very flexible, fast and heavily armed aircraft. It is called a multi-role aircraft, as it is capable of air defense, air strikes and air reconnaissance.

To perform a barrel roll: Fold both parts of the right wing downward, about 1 inch, and fold both parts of the left wing upward about 1 inch. Fold the tail fin flat down. Before launch, hold your plane about 4 inches from the front and throw gently forward. Your Tornado should spin on its axis and complete a barrel roll.

DASSAULT MIRAGE IVP

Make this marvelous Mirage fighter for your missions.

Use the printed page numbered 8 at the back of this book.

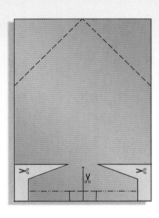

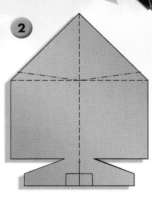

2. Now fold the pointed tip toward you using a valley fold along the straight line. Next, make two mountain folds along the diagonal lines by folding the pointed tip back on itself. Firmly fold the plane down its center, using a valley fold, ensuring that the folds in the pointed tip stay securely tucked in place.

1. Hold the page pattern-side down. Fold in the two top corners along the dotted lines using valley folds. Cut three slits at the bottom along the solid lines. Cut away the surplus tail section. Fold the outer flaps under using mountain folds and the inner flaps out using valley folds.

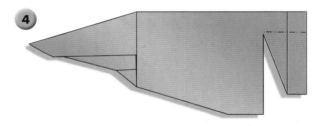

4. Fold up the wing tips using a valley fold and a mountain fold on each wing. Secure the tail by tucking the flap from one side around the other and interlock them.

To fly your plane, hold it about 3 inches from the front and throw it gently forward.

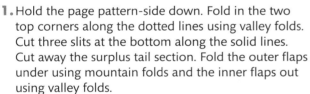

3. Cut a slit toward the front of the wings, shown by the solid line. Then, cut along the solid line to form the basic shape of the plane.

FACT

The Dassault Mirage IVP was a French jet-propelled supersonic aircraft. Although it could reach high speeds of up to Mach 2.2, its speed was restricted due to the temperature restrictions on its airframe.

To perform a loop: Fold the back edge of both wings sharply upward. Hold the base of the plane between your thumb and forefinger and throw firmly upward at a high angle. The nose of the plane should pitch upward and complete a loop.

LOCKHEED BOEING F-22 RAPTOR

A great jet fighter made in a few easy steps.

Use the printed page numbered 9 at the back of this book.

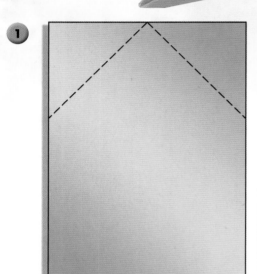

1. Hold the page pattern-side down. Fold in the two top corners along the dotted lines using valley folds.

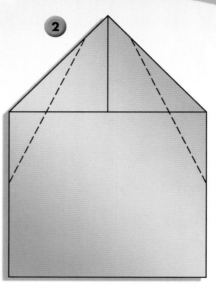

2. Fold along the two diagonal dotted lines, again using valley folds.

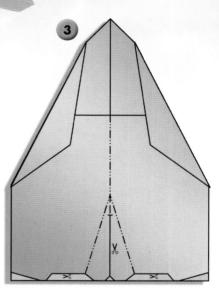

3. First, cut along the vertical solid line at the bottom. Cut away a small part of the tail along the solid lines, as shown. Make mountain folds and valley folds along the lines to form the shape of the plane.

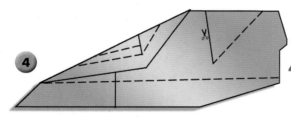

4. Make cuts on the wing along the solid lines. Valley folds along the dotted lines form the basic shape of the plane's body and wings.

To fly your plane, hold it about 4 inches from the front and throw it gently forward.

FACT

The F-22 is a semi-stealth fighter that uses the latest technology to out-fly and out-fight enemy aircraft. A combination of speed, stealth, high altitude and agility means that this aircraft is arguably the best fighter plane in the world.

To perform a high altitude flight: The F-22 Raptor can climb 40,000 feet a minute! See if you can launch your plane vertically into the air—hold the plane about 4 inches from the front and throw it fast and high above your head.

MCDONNELL DOUGLAS F-15 EAGLE

This bird-like plane will glide with ease.

Use the printed page numbered 10 at the back of this book.

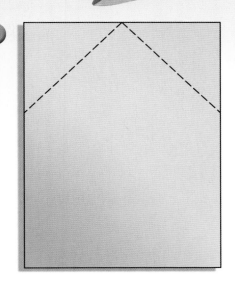

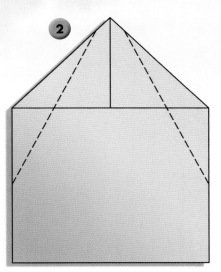

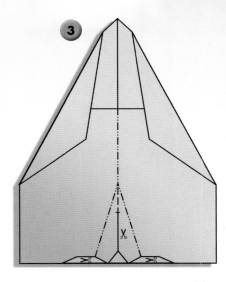

1. Hold the page pattern-side down. Fold in the two top corners along the dotted lines using valley folds.

2. Fold along the two diagonal dotted lines, again using valley folds.

3. First, cut along the vertical solid line at the bottom, as shown. Cut away the tail shape. Firmly fold the plane down its center using a mountain fold. Make sure you form a short valley fold by the slit, between the rear mountain folds.

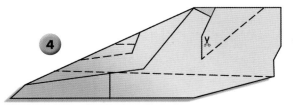

4. Make cuts on the wings along the solid lines, as shown. Using valley folds, fold along the dotted lines to create the shape of the wings.

To fly your plane, hold it about 4 inches from the front and throw it gently forward.

FACT
With a top speed of 1,875 mph (3,018 km/h), the F-15 Eagle can fly two and a half times the speed of sound. It is considered to be one of the most successful fighters with hundreds of combat victories and no losses in dogfights!

To perform in a dogfight: This aircraft needs to be fast and accurate to outwit its opponents in a dogfight. The small wings should help with this, but adding a paper clip to the end of the nose ensures that when it flies it is quick and accurate. Launch with a swift throw at any angle.

EUROFIGHTER TYPHOON

This plane is great for performing stunts!

Use the printed page numbered 11 at the back of this book.

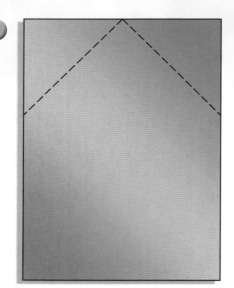

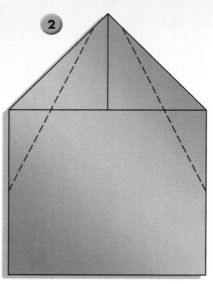

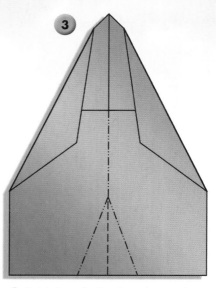

1. Hold the page pattern-side down. Fold in the two top corners along the dotted lines using valley folds.

2. Fold along the two diagonal dotted lines, again using valley folds.

3. Fold the whole plane in two by making mountain folds along the center line and the two small diagonals. Make a valley fold along the bottom section.

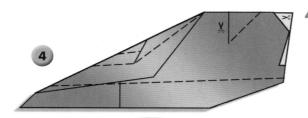

4. Cut away the tail, using the solid lines as a guide. Make cuts on the wings along the solid lines, as shown. Using valley folds, fold along the dotted lines to create the shape of the plane.

To fly your plane, hold it about 4 inches from the front and throw it gently forward.

FACT

The multi-role jet fighter, Typhoon, is used by many European air forces since its introduction in 2003, including the UK, Austria, Italy, Germany and Spain. It is a highly agile aircraft at both high and low speeds and can perform a variety of stunts, including rolls.

To perform a corkscrew roll: The corkscrew roll, or victory roll, is an extreme form of a barrel roll. Add a paper clip to the front of the left wing and launch the plane as if you were to throw a barrel roll, but throw the plane with more force and at a slight angle.

F-14 TOMCAT

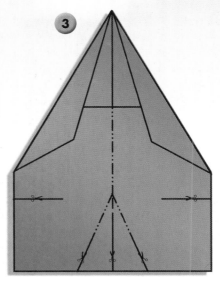

This impressive F-14 Tomcat will tear through the sky at top speed.

Use the printed page numbered 12 at the back of this book.

1. Hold the page pattern-side down. Fold the top corners along the dotted lines using valley folds.

2. Make two more valley folds along the diagonal dotted lines.

3. Using a pair of scissors, cut along the five solid lines, as shown. Make a mountain fold along the central line running down the plane. Make valley folds on the lines either side of the central fold, making sure you form a short valley fold between the two diagonal mountain folds at the rear of the plane.

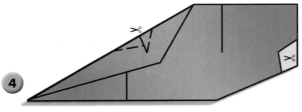

4. Next, cut around the tail and nose areas along the solid lines. Now make valley folds along the dotted lines.

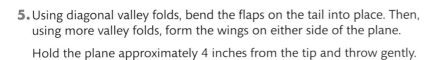

5. Using diagonal valley folds, bend the flaps on the tail into place. Then, using more valley folds, form the wings on either side of the plane.

Hold the plane approximately 4 inches from the tip and throw gently.

FACT

The Tomcat was the US Navy's premier carrier-based fighter. The swept wings, which can change for take-off and landing, and the upright tail fins give the Tomcat its distinctive appearance.

To perform a landing: The F-14 Tomcat needs a short landing to touch down on a carrier. Mark out two points in an open area and see if you can land your aircraft between the two points.

SEPECAT JAGUAR

The sensational Sepecat Jaguar is super speedy and easy to make.

Use the printed page numbered 13 at the back of this book.

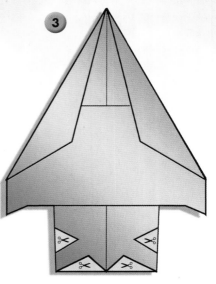

1. Hold the page pattern-side down. Using valley folds, fold the top corners along the dotted lines.

4. Fold in the tail along the vertical fold lines. Now make mountain folds along the three dashed lines running down the center of the plane. Make sure you form a short valley fold between the two diagonal mountain folds at the rear, keeping the tail pieces tucked inside as you fold.

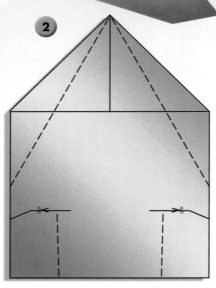

2. Make two more valley folds along the diagonal dotted lines. Using a pair of scissors, carefully cut along the solid lines. Now fold in the two flaps, along the dotted lines.

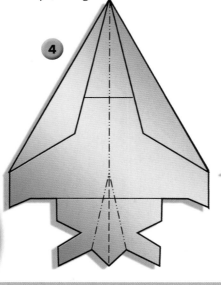

3. Using a pair of scissors, carefully cut away the four triangles to shape the tail fins.

5. Next form the wings by making the remaining valley folds on both sides of the plane's body. Finish the tail with diagonal folds.

To fly your plane, hold it approximately 4 inches from the tip and throw forward.

FACT

The Sepecat Jaguar was a joint French/British strike fighter and was flown by many air forces around the world. Its typical weapons include a rocket pod, bombs, cannons and missiles.

Accurate target practice: Set up a target, at first a larger object, such as a toilet roll. Throw your Sepecat Jaguar firmly forward and see if you can hit the target. Then, gradually make it harder with smaller objects.

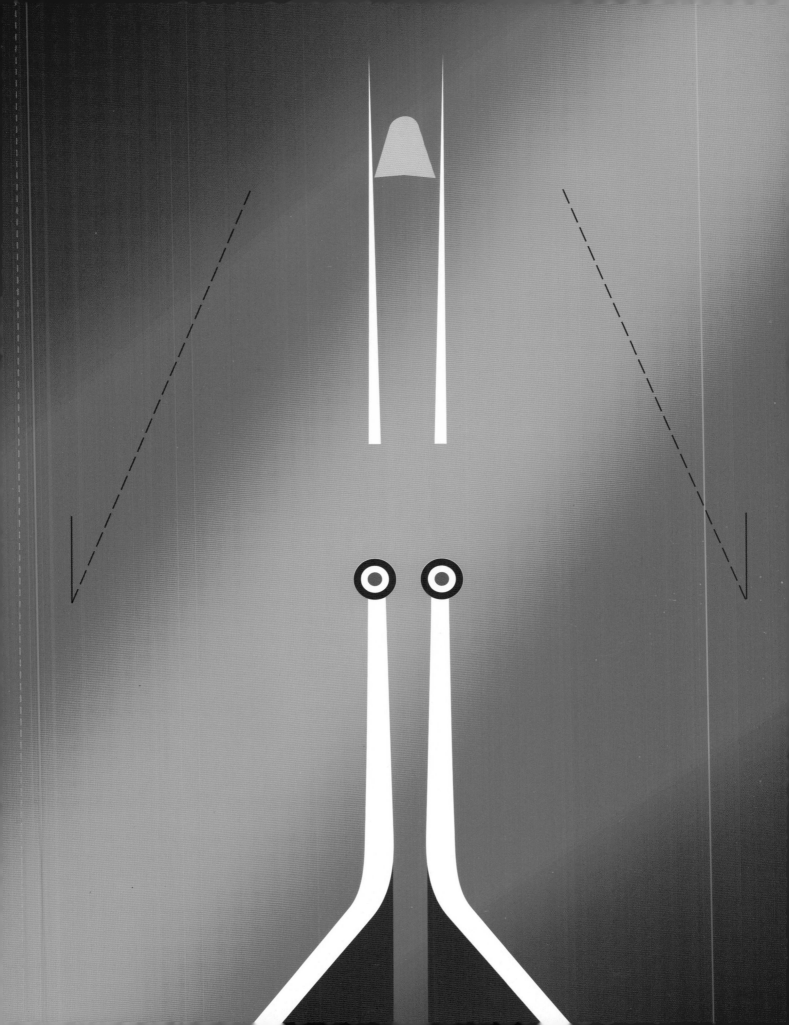

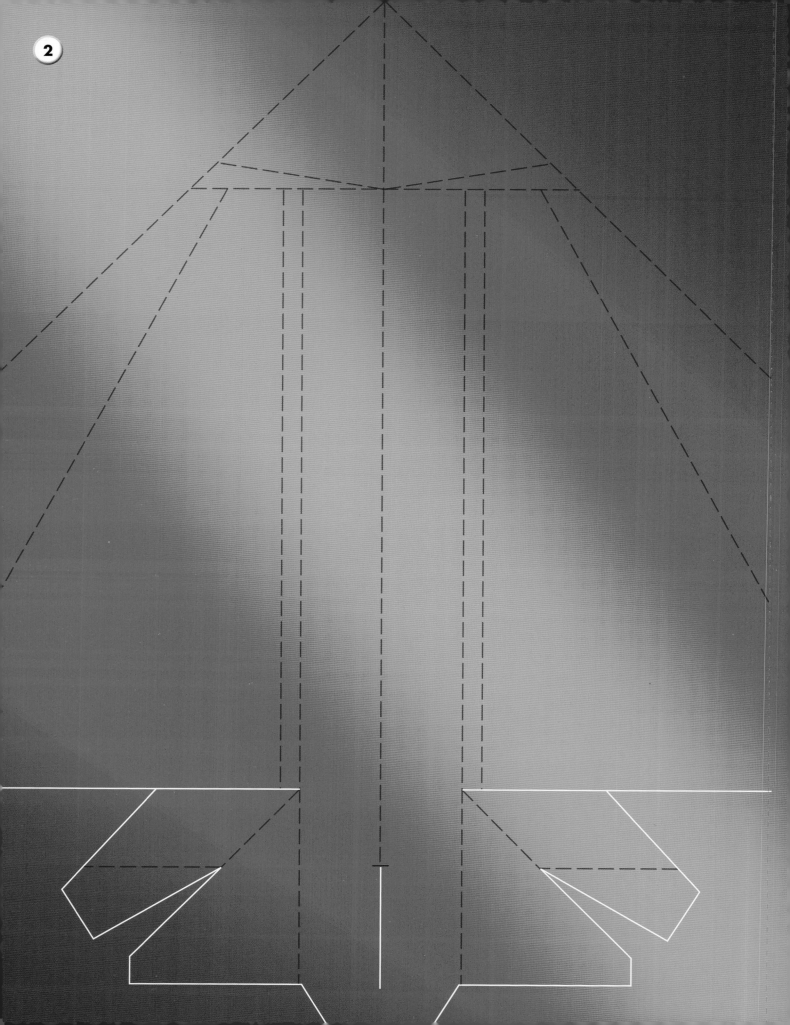

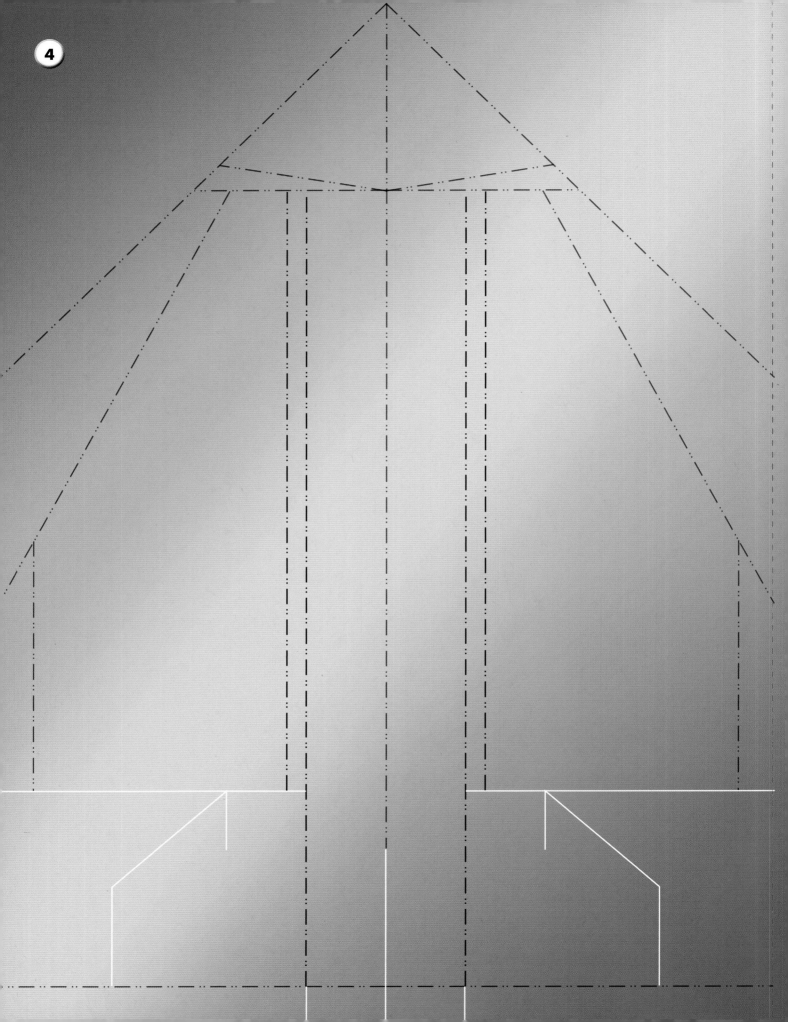

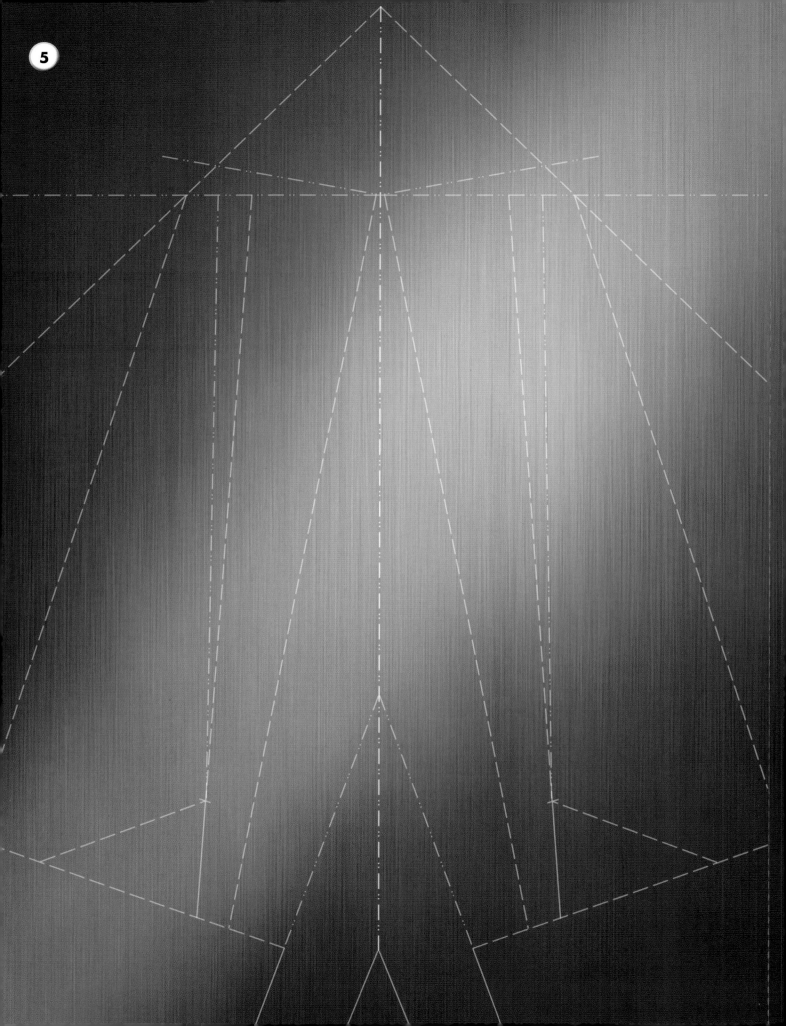

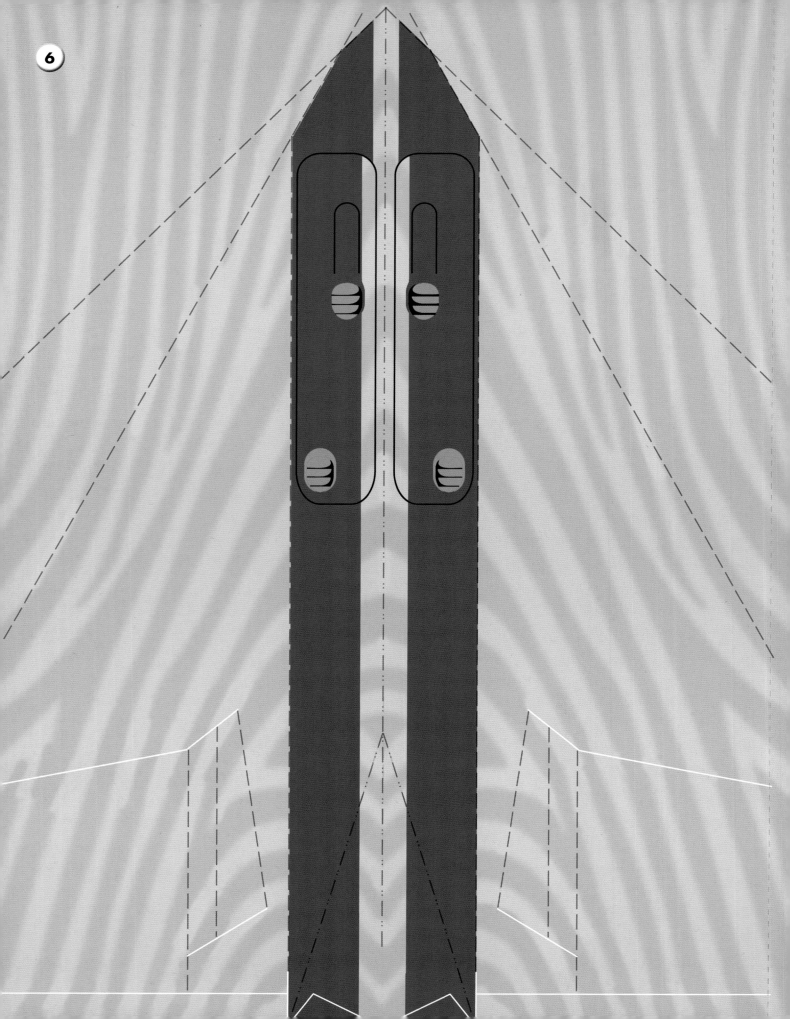

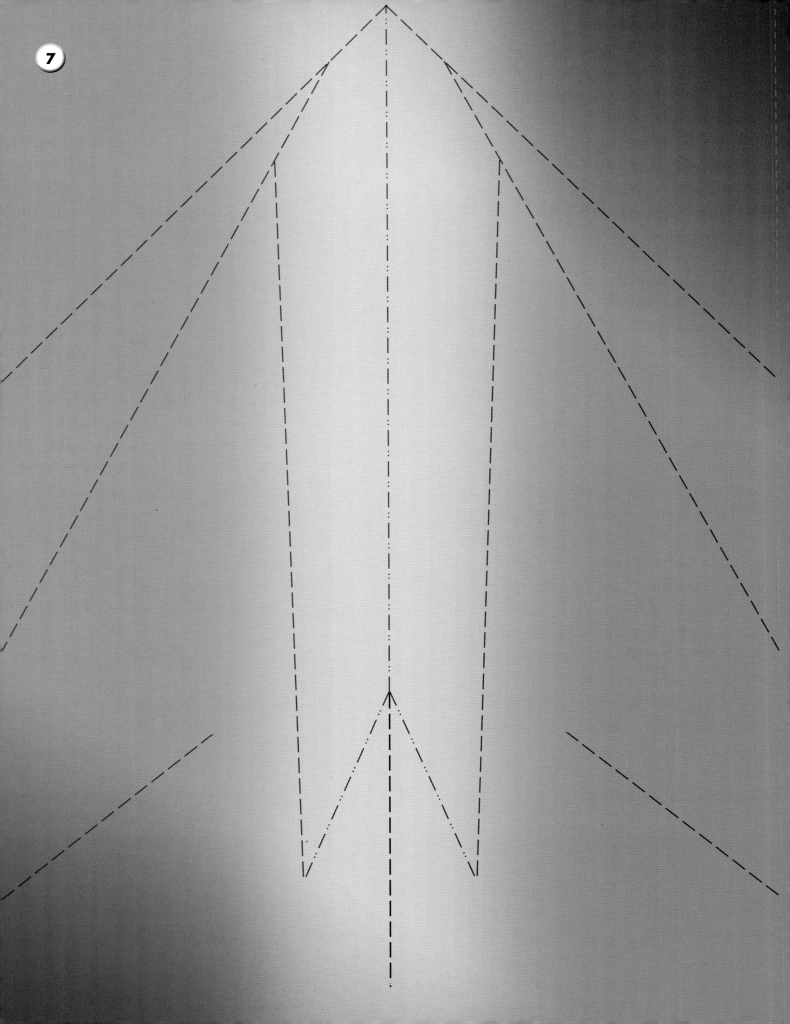

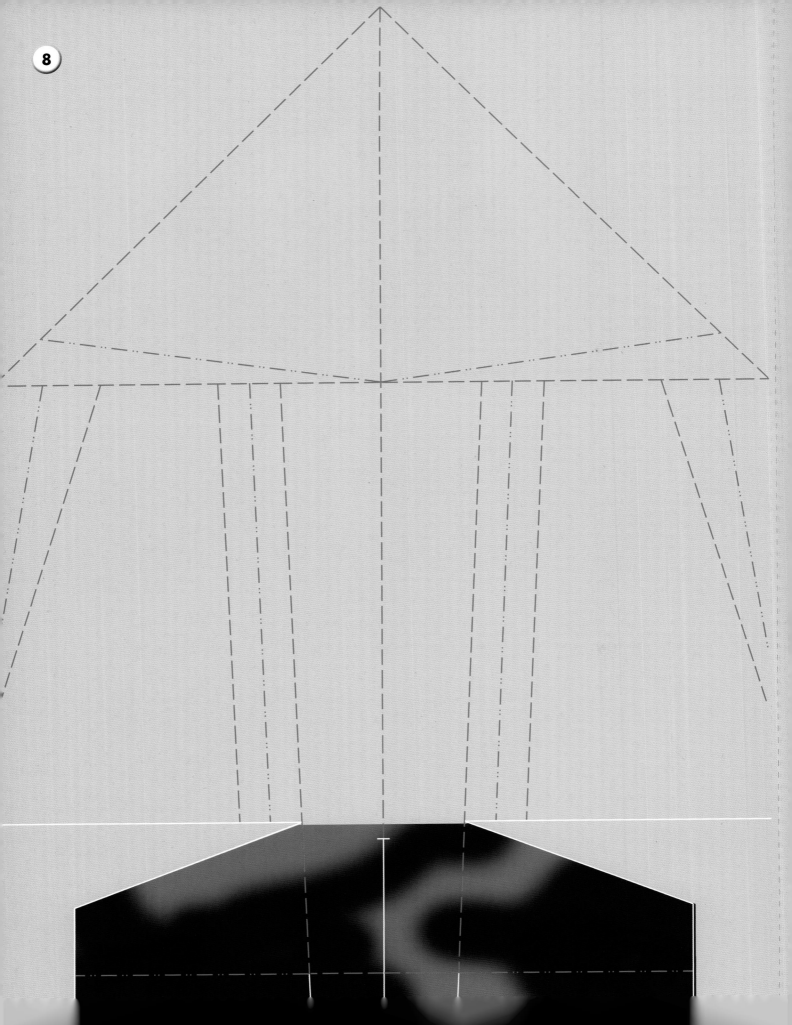

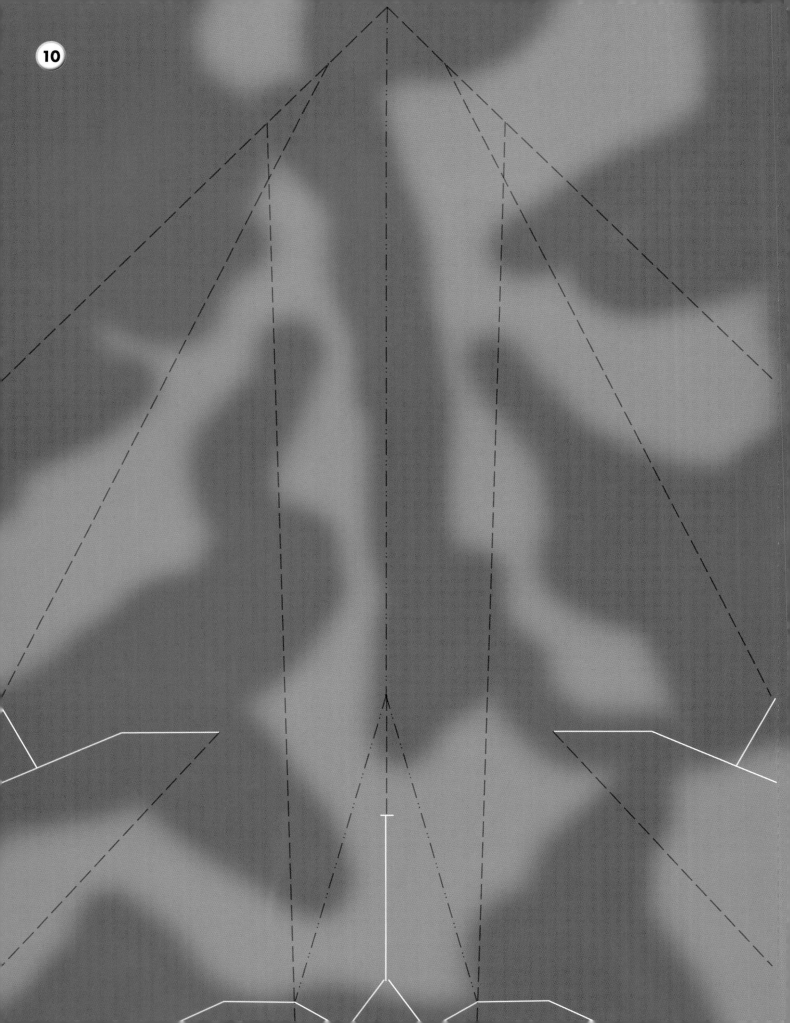

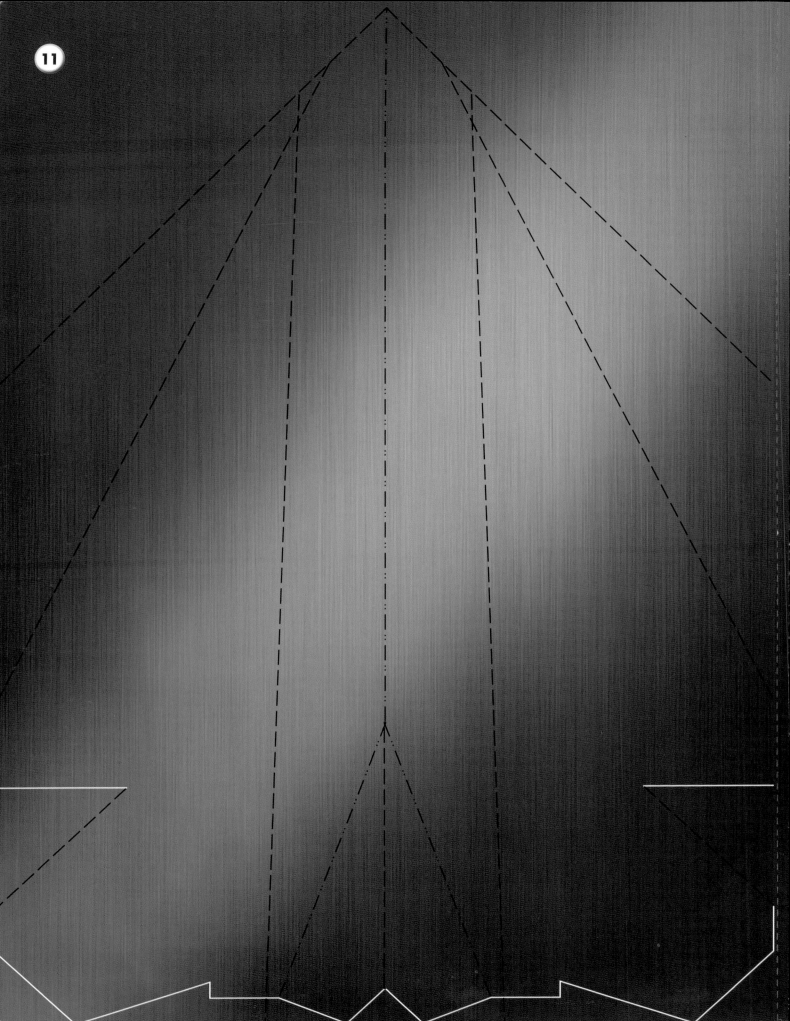

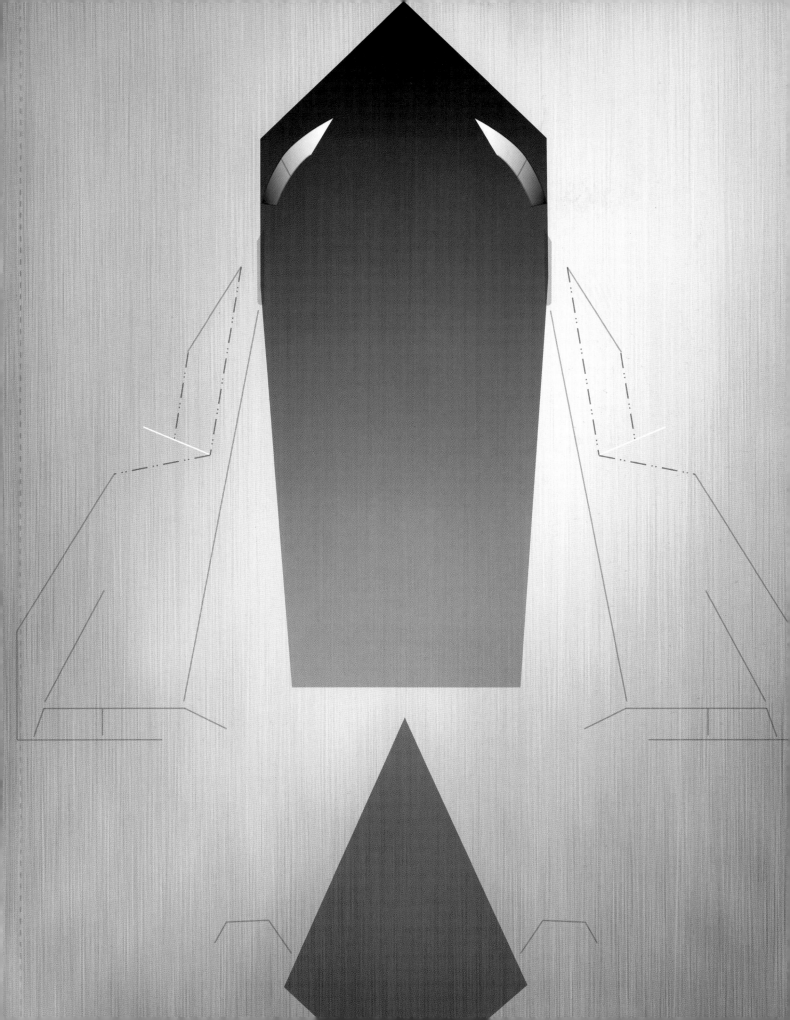

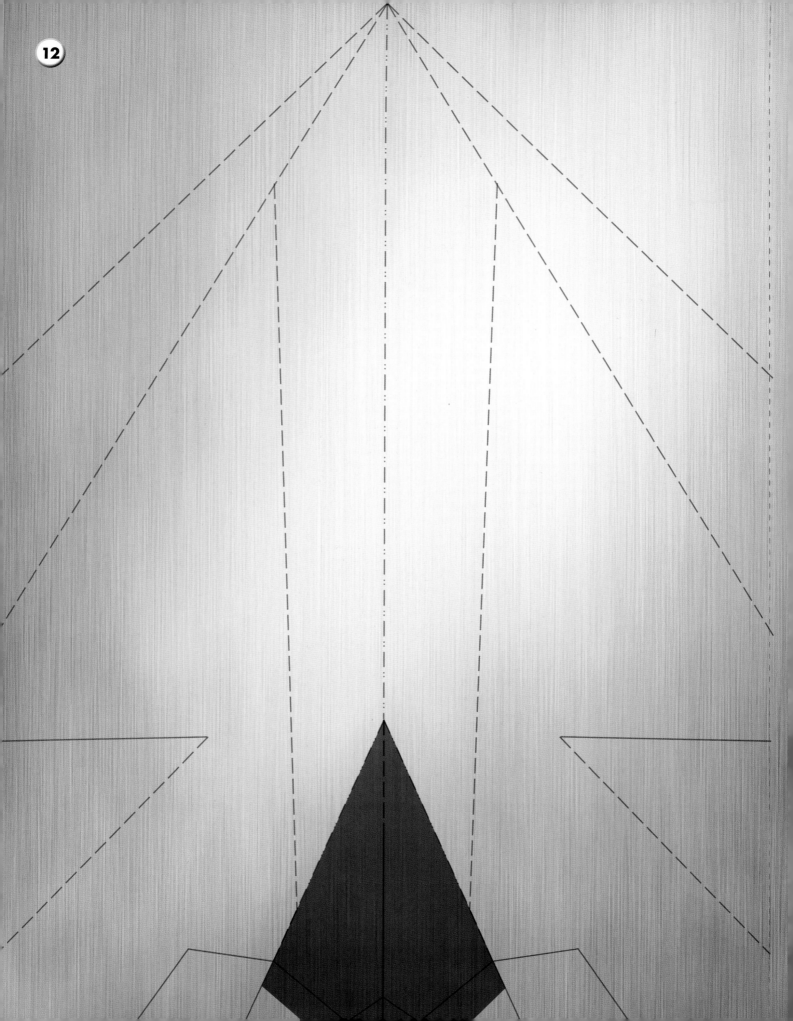

12

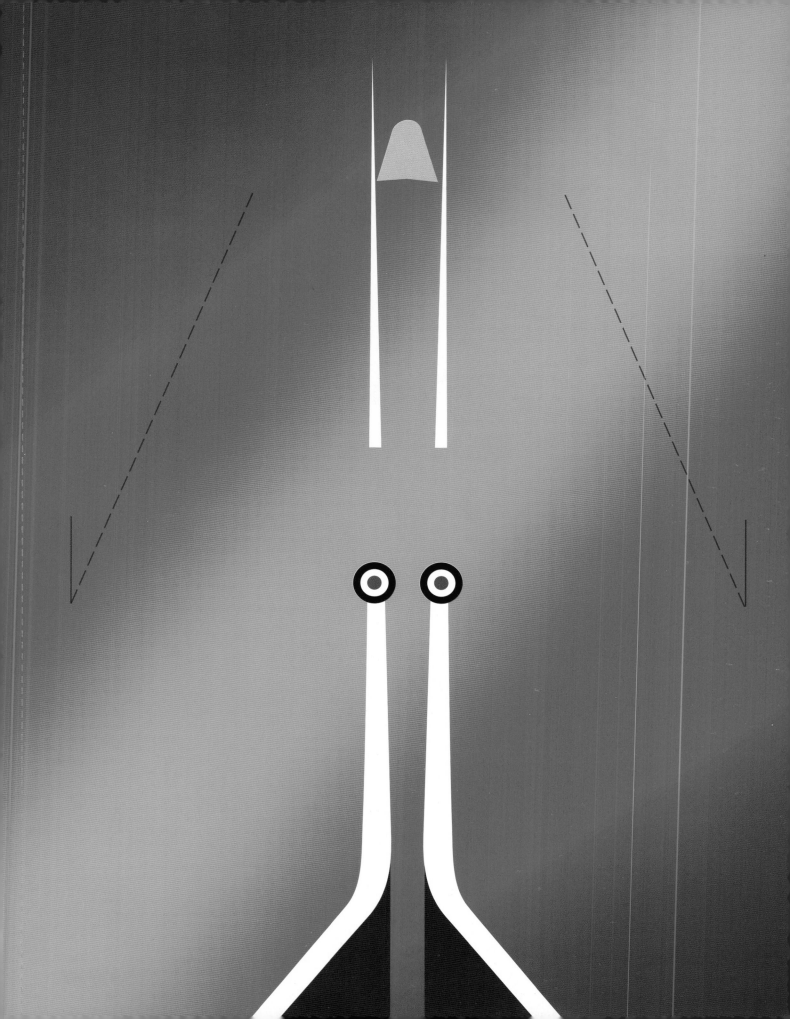

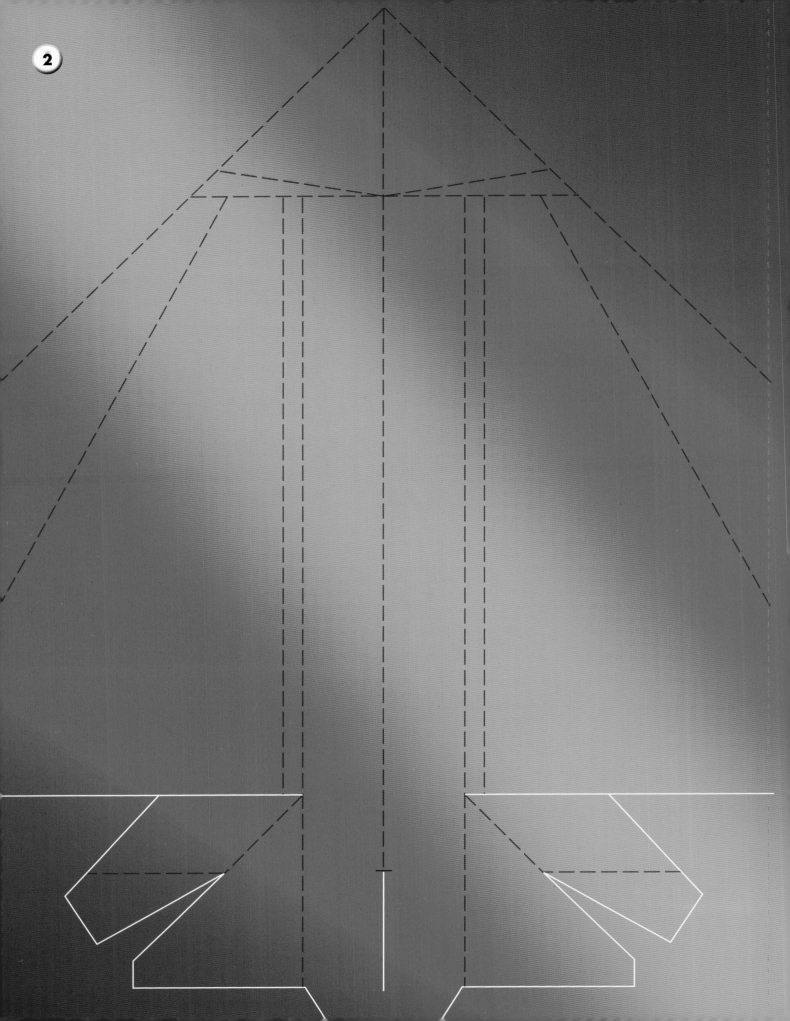

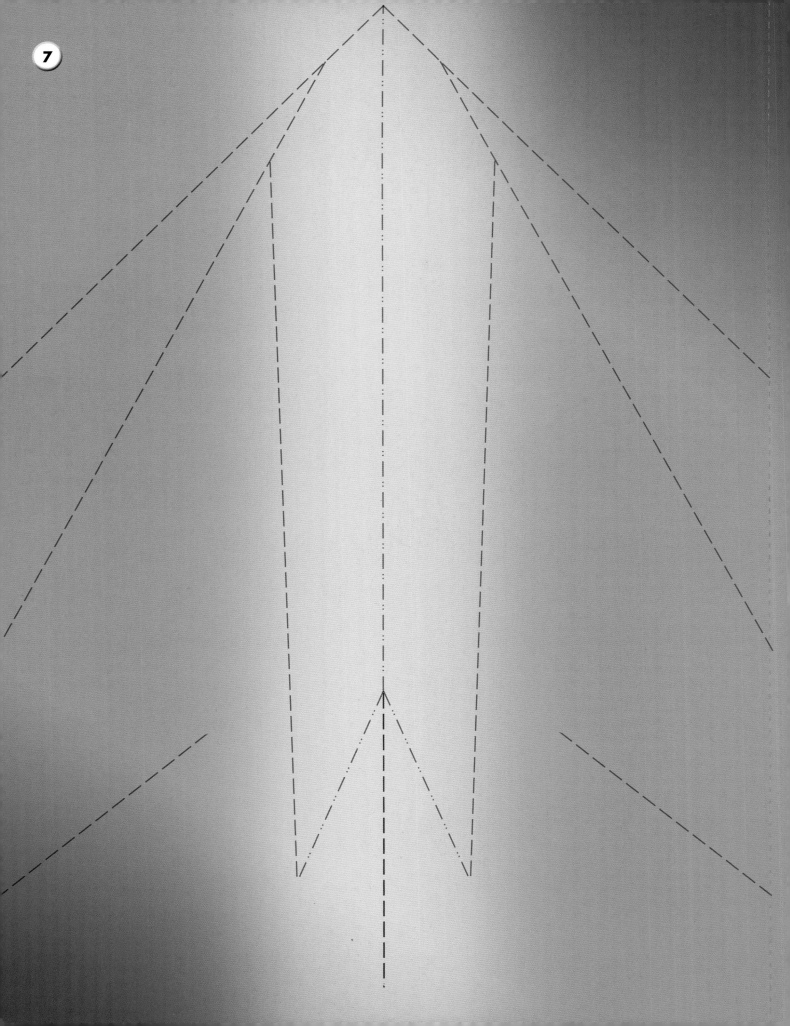